What Is Black and White?

by Miriam Sklar

ISBN: 978-1-338-75070-6

Illustrated by John Lund

Published by Scholastic Inc., 557 Broadway, New York, NY 10012

10 9 8 7 6 5 4 68 25 26 27/0

Printed in Jiaxing, China. First printing, January 2021.

A dog is black and white.

A penguin is black and white.

A cow is black and white.

A zebra is black and white.

A skunk is black and white.

A panda bear is black and white.

A snowman is black and white!